FRAMEWORKS CONSORTIUM

SCARY STORIES TO TELL IN THE BOARDROOM

VOLUME I

Frameworks Consortium Publishing

Frisco, TX 75035

Frameworks Consortium Publishing can bring authors to your live event. For more information or to book an event contact speaking@frameworksconsortiumpublishin g.com

For information about special discounts for bulk purchases, please contact orders@fra meworksconsortiumpublishing.com

Mayfield, George R.

Scary Stories to Tell in the Boardroom, Volume I / by George Mayfield, Frameworks Consortium

ISBN: 978-1-960225-05-4 (Paperback)

ISBN: 978-1-960225-06-1 (eBook-Kindle)

Subjects: Small Business Growth | Business Strategy | Entrepreneurship

Cover Design by: Sunshine Vizconde

Foreword by: Chris Honeycutt

Chapter Images created with Stable Diffusion generation model under open license

Printed in the United States of America

www.ScaryStoriesToTellInTheBoardroom.com

Contents

This book is dedicated to every entrepreneur who's ever stared into the abyss of uncertainty, armed only with their passion and a cup of coffee. To the visionaries who turn the mundane into magic and the impossible into the inevitable. To those who don't just read scary stories, but live them, learn from them, and laugh in the face of them. Here's to you, the beautiful dreamers and daring doers - may your business be the greatest adventure of your life.

Introduction

by George Mayfield

It was a dark and stormy night- No, really! There were around two or three dozen professionals from various sectors convened in a room at the nearby community college campus. The event was organized to hear Jeffrey Brewster, a Chartered Financial Analyst, discuss his journey as a business leader and the obstacles he encountered along the way. The inclement weather, coupled with the familiarity amongst many participants, created an uncharacteristic lively atmosphere, transforming the event from a formal presentation to a more engaging, interactive session. As each thunderclap echoed, participants contributed their own anecdotes, adding to the richness of the discussion.

As the rain continued to lash down outside, I found myself thinking that we were essentially a group of adults sharing stories around a campfire, only these stories were real, and a campfire would likely break a few laws and safety codes. I jokingly suggested that it would make a great premise for a business book. Little did I know that my joke would evolve into a hypothetical idea and eventually become a concrete project.

For nearly one year, I petitioned my network for stories and authors. I got a few laughs and even a couple of people told me that it was a terrible idea. But I was persistent. Over time, the project began to take shape. Finally, I was able to assemble a team of clever and ingenuitive business professionals who were all eager to share their stories in an unusual way.

Thus, I present to you "Scary Stories to Tell in the Boardroom". It's a collection of tales, tips, and strategies from professionals who strive to help business owners and leaders face their worst fears head-on and triumph. Each chapter is a unique, standalone story that will paint a bloodcurdling picture of the common struggles between businesses and their owners with a bit of extra "strange and unusual".

We hope that through these stories readers will find solace in knowing that they are not alone, and perhaps even gain insights to help them with their own business journey.

Foreword: B-Flicks to Boardrooms: A Horror Fan's Take on Business Strategy

by Chris Honeycutt

As a long-time fan of the horror genre and a seasoned professional in the banking industry, I find myself uniquely positioned to appreciate the genius behind "Scary Stories to Tell in the Boardroom." This book, a riveting fusion of business strategies and haunting tales of corporate missteps, is as unconventional as it is enlightening.

I fondly recall my days working for Roger Cormann, immersed in the world of horror, and little did I know that the skills I honed then would come in handy in the relatively staid realm of banking. Not only has my love for horror, particularly the charmingly cheesy classics from the '70s and '80s, followed me into my banking career, but it has also enriched my perspective on business growth strategies.

Horror, as a genre, has always dared to push boundaries and challenge societal norms. It forces us to confront our deepest fears and asks us, "What if it was real?" or "What if it really happened?" It is this aspect of horror that connects so seamlessly with the world of business. In a sense, running a business is like navigating a horror story. It can be fraught with uncertainty, challenges, and fear, and yet, it can also be an exhilarating adventure.

In my years as a relationship manager for a bank, I have guided many a business owner through the winding paths of business growth. I have seen firsthand the fear that comes with the territory – fear of failure, fear of making the wrong decisions, fear of the unknown. It is a horror story of its own, and yet, it is rarely addressed in conventional business texts. This is where "Scary Stories to Tell in the Boardroom" sets itself apart.

This book offers a fresh take on business education, presenting it through the lens of horror. It is a genre that I had never imagined would have such a profound connection with the corporate world. But the more I ponder it, the more I realize how well they align.

The tales in this book are terrifying not because they are fictional horrors, but because they are real-world business mistakes, mishaps, and missteps. It is the reality of these stories, the chilling truth that these could very well be your own business horror stories, that makes them so impactful.

However, it's not all doom and gloom. "Scary Stories to Tell in the Boardroom" provides invaluable lessons and strategies that can help you navigate the perils of the business world. It teaches business owners to face their fears head-on and to take action against them, rather than being paralyzed by them.

I am delighted to have been able to contribute to this groundbreaking project and am confident that "Scary Stories to Tell in the Boardroom" will serve as a beacon for business owners in these challenging times. This book entertains as it educates, and I believe it will be a valuable resource for anyone looking to build a successful business.

Remember, seeking help is not a sign of weakness, but a strategic move towards growth. And in this endeavor, Frameworks Consortium stands as an unparalleled resource, ready to guide professionals at every step. As you delve into these eerie tales of business horror, I hope you find solace in knowing that help is just an arm's stretch away.

Here's to a thrilling ride through the terrifying yet exciting world of business. Hold on tight, and let's begin our journey with "Scary Stories to Tell in the Boardroom."

The Invincible Man

by Jeff Sandene

The warehouse was cold, and dark. A chill wind blew through its vast spaces. Even the faint lights overhead, flickering, did little to pierce the ambient gloom. Caroline walked forward with a flashlight, her breath fogging in the wintry air. She was bundled in a heavy work coat, but even so, the chill of the air in the building seeped into the depths of her bones.

She had to prepare. Prepare for the sale. Another sale. Endless sales. All this stuff... she looked around. The flashlight swung its cold and lonely circle of light on the piles and piles of inventory. Helmets. Water bottles. T-shirts. Stacks of promotional balls.

All of it worthless.

Caroline remembered the beginning. She was in her 50s now. She remembered being in her 30s and 40s. It had all been a dream, a beautiful, lavish dream, a dream of silk and gossamer and gold. A dream of vacations, homes, fancy parties, VIP sports events. A dream. A beautiful dream.

But she'd woken up. And now it was dark and cold.

"Caroline..."

A crawling, creeping voice, like the cold frigid air. She heard it. Or thought she did. Her teeth chattered.

"Caroline..."

Seeping like frost on the North wind, the voice stretched out into her ears. So cold. So cold.

She shivered. She turned. The light of the flashlight bounced around the heaps of product, around the darkened avenues of the stock. Inventory she had to sell. How much would any of this sell for? Any of these things? $40? $30? $20? Less than that? She remembered when it had sold in the hundreds, thousands of dollars. All of it. But that was before. Before it had all withered and died.

"Caroline..."

She swirled about, her coat hovering in the dead air.

A thing was there.

A dead thing.

Translucent, like glass. She could see through it, a haunting thing of ice. A cold and lonely thing. A dead thing.

Her dead thing.

"Richard!" she shouted; her voice swallowed by the thick cold air.

The ghost lurched forward, hovering, not touching the ground. The spirit, the specter, the phantom—it lilted forward in the air, moving in a dreamlike way. A nightmarish way, more like. It was an apparition that looked like Richard. But how was that so? Richard had been dead for more than a year now.

"Caroline..." said the spirit. It smiled, but that made it more frightening. "How is the liquidation going..."

"It's... it's going well, Richard." said Caroline, almost amazed at how easily she was talking with a ghost. "I should... the auditors and the lawyers say we should have the rest of the goods sold in the next two years. Though..." Caroline bunched her coat around her, "it hasn't gotten any easier since you...Since you died" that last part sounding more like a question.

"It was... worth so much..." Richard's voice sounded like air being forced through forest trees and felt cold as winter.

"It was, Richard, it was," said Caroline. She grimaced. Nothing was being sold for anything close to what it had been worth before. It was hard enough to find outlets and memorabilia stores that would take larger volumes.

She narrowed her eyes. "How couldn't you have known? You had associations with that... that athlete. He was the only name that mattered for your firm. Our company. How could you work so closely with him, and not know what an awful human being he was?"

"He was... famous..."

"Yes! But that's what brought it all down, Richard!" She wanted to check herself. This wasn't real. She was seeing things because of the cold. But she couldn't help but yell, couldn't help but take out all the frustrations of all these years that had built. It all came tumbling out. "He was so famous that when all that abuse... all those sexual crimes... when it all came out, everyone knew. He was so famous that he had so far to fall, and he fell all that way."

"Yes..."

"And we fell with him." She scowled. "You only ever did business with him. His name. His face. His products. His autograph. Couldn't you have worked harder to make deals with other athletes? If... Richard, if we had had other athletes... if you had sponsored other athletes, the enterprise wouldn't have fallen along with him. We could have survived."

Richard hovered. His translucent face – was there remorse there? It was hard to tell.

"Oh, the luxury, the luxury!" Caroline was now caught in her own fantasies, her eyes suddenly far away. "Oh, I remember the jet. It was so pretty, and so quiet in the air. I remember the house in Malibu, and the one in Montana. I remember the box seats at the stadium." She sighed. "At least the boys and Tiffany managed to get through private school before we weren't able to pay for that anymore." She grimaced, bitter feelings coursing through her veins. "I'm living in a small apartment now, Richard. That's all I can afford. That's all there is left."

The specter hovered there in silence, seeming to eye her with amusement. Finally, its rasping voice spoke: "Didn't mean to die..."

"Well, you should have taken better care of yourself, Richard," said Caroline. "You always said you'd lose weight, start eating healthy, but you never did. I should have seen that heart attack coming. You always used to huff and puff going down the stairs. I should have made you work harder to stay healthy."

"We were successful...enjoying life..."

"And we didn't even have any life insurance." Caroline went on, not seeming to hear her dead husband. "With your health, I suppose I... I wish you had thought of it. It would have made things easier for me, and the children. Now..." Caroline glanced around the storehouse. All the piled product. All the inventory. "I'm still having such a hard time, Richard. It's been decades since I worked. I'm not used to managing things like this."

"Sorry...I didn't think it would end...I didn't think it would end this way...He wasn't supposed to ...I wasn't supposed to ..."

"We should have done a better job investing, while you were alive. All our money... we just put it back into the company and into our lifestyle...Your lifestyle! Margaret... she tried to get us to talk to her financial adviser. We didn't. You wouldn't. We should have, but we didn't. We thought the company would be enough... that's what you thought, what you said." She glared at the phantom of her husband. "You were wrong."

The phantom floated, suspended just a few feet away from her. It was deep and dark in the night of the warehouse. Caroline's teeth chattered. She could feel. Feel the ruin of the place. Feel the ruin of the organization her husband had run, which had started with such promise but ended in such disaster. Everything was dead.

With a terrible chill up her spine, Caroline realized that her husband and his firm were both dead, dead, and rotting. Her husband was dead, rotting in his grave, his body a festering corpse eaten by maggots and grubs, oozing and bloating. It was dead. And the company? This was its corpse. She was standing in its corpse.

She was standing in the dead body of her husband's venture.

And in that one terrible moment she had a sensation of all the products around her rotting like dead flesh. Oozing, bloating, eaten by maggots, falling apart in a dead and decaying heap. She looked at the heap of product, and it seemed to squirm. She shrieked in terror. The maggots were eating it here! The dead body of her husband's company. She was standing in the middle of death!

"Caroline..."

"Stop it! Stop it!" she shouted at the apparition. "Don't haunt me! Don't haunt me, Richard! You ran your business into the ground. You ran your body into the ground. You left me and the children all alone. You've done enough damage! Go be dead and leave me in peace!"

A horrible dark wind blew through the warehouse. A black and wicked air that smelled of death and the noxious scents of a coffin. She seemed to hear terrible laughter, and a horrible ghostly cackle that rose from the ground like it was coming up from Hell. Was it her husband? She couldn't tell. His ghost was in front of her--

But then it was gone. In the blink of an eye the phantom had vanished. The specter was suddenly gone, and Caroline was left all by herself in the cold and empty warehouse, shivering in the midst of all the worthless merchandise she would have to sell for next to nothing.

Caroline blinked. She looked around. Everything was as it had been. Pallets of boxes with bright orange stickers showing what had already been audited, what was left to count. Here and there empty and ripped boxes, snack wrappers and empty bottles left from the crew. All she smelled now was the dank smell of a warehouse. All that remained from her altercation was the biting cold.

Did it really even happen, or was it just the stress? She wasn't used to working. Not like this. She thought of Richard again. She knew he loved her, but she also knew that he struggled with knowing how to take care of her. Maybe he thought the lifestyle was enough. But it was gone now. The life she lived was gone.

She shivered. The cold air was in her bones. She wondered if she, too, would die soon. But she had work to do, while she was still above ground. So much to still do. So, she shivered, and moved the flashlight, and began to resume her trek through the piles of merchandise, cataloging the inventory for the sale. The auditors, she knew, would be there by morning.

Author's Afterward

Richard found success in his business. And maybe more success than he thought would ever happen. But Richard didn't manage his success. And he didn't plan for succession. As his business grew, so did his tastes. He grew ever confident that there was only one direction to go and that was up. He didn't think about his own death nor the downfall of his business. He didn't consider how his family would be affected if the income stopped.

Many times, business owners get so caught up in the success of their business, that they don't think about their personal finances. They don't consider themselves an employee of their own company – they ARE the company! So, they don't set up personal finance plans that take care of themselves or their family when it comes time to separate from that company.

Owning and running a business is hard work but can be very rewarding. It is important to reach out to experts that can help you reward yourself and ensure that the hard work you put in is spent in the best way possible for yourself and your family.

JEFF SANDENE is a certified exit planner (CEPA) and financial planner (CFP). His team specializes in helping business owners turn their company wealth into personal wealth as they transition towards retirement.

Visit www.sandenestrategies.com to obtain valuable resources such as weekly market commentaries and other useful tools or to schedule an introductory chat. Visualize your Fabulous Future today!

The Headless IT Guy

by Paul Feather

Sam sat hunched over his computer as the world around him grew dark. He looked at his watch. It was only a little after 6:30. Why was it suddenly as dark as night?

Sam shuddered and realized that it was unusually cold for an office building at this time of year. He considered hunting around for the thermostat. Perhaps it was stuck in a cooling cycle. The temperature had been comfortable barely half an hour ago, but now his thin white button-up was leaving him exposed to the looming chill of the air. Sam was dressed in the normal clothes of an IT administrator. He wore no special badges or signifiers. He was assigned this common cubicle among all the other IT workers. The database administrators, the coders, even the helpdesk people were all in this area. And this area is just where he needed to be.

He took a sip of his coffee, expecting to find some comfort, and grimaced. It, too, was ice cold. Sam thought he'd better get up and get a fresh cup and maybe get his blood pumping. He had been staring at his screen for so long, focused on the task at hand.

He stood up and looked over the cubicle wall. He had to blink a few times to get his eyes to adjust to the darkness. It really was very dark for an office — even with the lights out. Why were the lights out? There was usually a glow from ambient light from copy machines, power strips, and other miscellaneous equipment, but the darkness seemed to extinguish all but the glow from his own laptop.

Darkness and cold—they had come as a pair. How long had he been sitting at his desk, in his cubicle, typing away? He checked his watch again. As if to emphasize his curiosity, the digital numbers changed right on the minute. 6:33.

Sam was a mid-level IT Administrator relocated from another branch because his wife took a job in this city. He was a hit with all the other IT employees from his first day in the office. For the last few months since his arrival, the morning breakroom would be abuzz with Sam's jokes and relatable stories he called "stupid human tricks" about dealing with hapless end-users. Everyone seemed to love his presence. He was simply one of their own. It wasn't long before they began opening up to him, telling him their own stories and the secret ins and outs of the office politics.

Sam peered in the darkness. There was no one in sight. It really wasn't that late. Any other company of this size would have at least a few people working at this hour, but there wasn't even a bustle of a night cleaning crew. Even the hum that would be from the overcompensating air conditioner was absent. It was very disconcerting.

It only added to the sense that Sam had sometimes that he was just a stranger within this company. It was a feeling based in truth. No one he worked with knew who he really was or the actual reason that put him here. Sam liked his new co-workers, but he knew better than to get attached. He wouldn't be here long and liking them too much would make his secret task more difficult. The truth was, he needed them to like him, and this hunt had proven to be particularly difficult. He should have been able to move on by now and his desperation was causing him to put in these extra hours.

Sam didn't work at this company at all. He wasn't a mid-level IT Administrator, although he had been in the past. He had been brought in as a consultant by the Chief Information Officer of this company in complete secrecy. The company was in dire straits. It had failed numerous IT audits, and its troubles had spilled into the public view, resulting in a drastic deflation of the stock price. The CIO had been warned that this would happen and now his job was on the line.

The trouble was, that there were no basic controls within many of the systems that ran the company. Specifically, there were no separation of duties among the users in various departments. It seemed that everyone with a computer had access to every other department's information. Sales, HR records, and even financial information was accessible to any user that knew how to navigate the system. IT management knew this was a problem, but had been unable to fix it. No auditor would ever give a passing score to a company operating in this manner. It's what they referred to as a massive "Red-flag".

Sam had successfully infiltrated the IT department. Finding holes in IT compliance was just as much about the people as it was about the systems they operated. And the more he was here, the more he wandered the halls as a supposedly lowly employee, the more confused he got. The team had divulged their frustrations in upper management. They expected 100% uptime and would get especially nasty when they couldn't work from home or wherever their travels led them. They wanted to simply open their laptops and get right to work and shouldn't have to click a link in their email or open a dual authentication app on their phone. Jobs were threatened every time they had to call the help desk.

At the same time, the IT team knew they had to pass the audit. Sam worked shoulder to shoulder with the team to fix the code. Many times, it would get fixed. They'd run tests and pass. They'd celebrate with a happy hour at the bar down the street. The next morning, it would be all back to the way it was. Whatever they did would be reversed and recreating that code wouldn't work a second time. The team was very helpful, but they would get strangely silent when Sam would start asking questions about who wrote the code. They would never offer to stay late with him, either. By 5, 5:30, everyone would be gone. It was odd. Very odd.

He shivered. The darkness seemed to be growing. Who wrote the code? A clue Sam hadn't been able to uncover yet. Wait. Right! The very problem they were trying to fix gave him access to HR files. Coffee can wait.

Sam plopped back down and hunched over his screen, like a beacon of stark white light in the shadows. The darkness was quiet, and the world was cold, but Sam clicked away, digging deep into the HR systems. Recently fired employees. Of course. This could be it! It was something of a classic tale: somebody in the IT department getting fired, or not even fired—just getting frustrated and fed up with the unreasonable demands of the company. They would be fired, or take 'time off,' and then turn around and use their skills and their remaining days of IT access to sabotage the company. Had that happened now? Was there an employee recently fired that was activating programs and resetting all users access back to the "all access" settings every day, just to get revenge on the company that had given them the boot? Sam needed to identify the culprit. After all, this was what he was getting paid for.

And yet there was no clear sign...

He kept scanning through 1000's of pages of employee access rights looking for a disgruntled employee who could be doing this level of infiltration and sabotage. They would need to have elevated administrative access to the company and its network. It would have to be someone with the right kind of security clearance, maybe even somebody who still had access to the company's campus. He was cross-checking recently terminated employees with the permissions they had been assigned while actively employed, trying to see if there was a good match for the potential saboteur.

The darkness and cold was growing. His breath was like a dense fog into the glow of his computer screen.

Then, he saw movement. Perhaps it was his breath. What the hell? How was it so cold?

He stood up again. Through the darkness he saw a man approaching and had to blink. The darkness must be playing tricks. The man came closer, now only six feet away from him. A man without a head.

Sam screamed at the top of his lungs.

Sam instinctively grabbed his laptop, slamming it shut. He ran for the exit as fast as he could. He glanced back over his shoulder. He got a good glimpse of the man. He had a white shirt on, and he wore slacks, and he was tall and gangly, and the shirt was stained. Stained with blood?

Sam turned the corner, then he slumped down in terror to the floor, afraid out of his mind, not believing what he was seeing. A headless man! A headless man!

In his panic, Sam looked down at his computer screen. There was a striking figure currently sitting in the 'Other' section of the Human Resources file screen that he had been looking at. It was a badge photo of a tall, gangly man with a white shirt. An odd looking man that seemed to never smile. Still, in his terror, Sam didn't lose his wits. He began to type rapidly and clicked his trackpad to determine what had happened to this particular employee. He had to be in the 'Other' section for a reason; past employees weren't placed there if they were simply terminated under normal circumstances.

It turned out that this particular employee had... died. He had been caught in a terrifying elevator accident and had lost his head. But what was he doing walking around without a head? Sam rapidly typed away.

The air around him began to glow suddenly, an infernal green aura, and as he glanced around the corner, sure enough, there was the headless man. A fierce blaze of green light now emanated from the neck of the headless man in a contorted, almost head-like shape.

The headless man began to rumble towards him. Sam screamed again. He grabbed his laptop and ran, ran down the hallway to his right, and made a beeline for the exit as fast as he could.

Out in his car, with the seat leaned back as far as it would go, Sam began to work more tirelessly than ever through the code that controlled the company's user access policies. And that's when he started to notice something odd. Line by line, segment by segment, the code was riddled with these odd characters. Strangely shaped. Not normal letters, not even in other languages. They didn't even match the Cyrillic alphabet. Sam copied and pasted one into the browser's search.

He was immediately taken to a number of fringe conspiracy websites. The most 'reputable' of the ones he could find seemed to indicate that these strange symbols, or at least the one he had copied and searched, belonged to the language of an ancient, antediluvian civilization ruled by half-angel monsters that practiced infernal magic.

What?

He kept on searching. Something about dark magic practiced in the world before the Flood, and an idea that one could access this ancient power by making use of these symbols. Sam, frankly, was more than a little fascinated by these writings. He wasn't much of a conspiracy guy. But then again, he wasn't a guy who believed in ghosts or monsters either, yet he had seen the man without a head. He kept reading and digging for more.

As wild as it was, and as little as he believed it, it all clicked into place. Some ex-employee, or some cabal of employees, had discovered a way to code with this magical set of codes. They had used it to raise the dead! That's why they were able to continually reinstall the older access settings of the organization! That's why they could make such immense changes on what seemed like a regular basis, without themselves ever setting foot on campus! This headless IT employee was rising from his grave every night, going into the IT department, and undoing all of Sam's compliance efforts!

It had to be stopped!

Of course, knowing is half the battle. Now that he knew what he was looking for, Sam could work at warp speed. He ran a new script through the system, this time specifically designed to keep out any "undead" users. Of course, he knew how to do this—it was amazing what you learn from years of experience.

He remembered the headless man in the dark. He shuddered and he hit 'Enter' on the keyboard. He hoped he was safe. He hoped the company was safe. He hoped he had done what was right.

Author's Afterward

Separation of duties (SOD) is an important security principle for IT systems to help to ensure that critical tasks and operations are divided among multiple individuals. This is particularly essential from a compliance perspective that companies follow the principle of least privilege, which is a concept in computer security that limits users' access rights to only what are strictly required to do their jobs. Users are granted permission to read, write or execute only the files or resources necessary to do their jobs. It minimizes the risk of errors or fraud occurring due to a single individual having too much control.

Having SOD in place means that multiple levels of individuals are needed to complete a process or task. This not only reduces the risk of errors but helps organizations adapt to industry regulations and standards. By assigning separate roles and responsibilities to different people, an organization can minimize the potential for unintended consequences due to one person having too much control over a single process or system.

SOD is just as important from an operational perspective because it helps organizations protect themselves from internal fraud or mistakes made by employees who have too much access to privileged information. Ultimately, separation of duties provides greater security, transparency, and accountability for organizations. It is a key component of any cybersecurity or compliance strategy and should be taken seriously by companies of all sizes and industries.

PAUL FEATHER is a Certified Information Systems Auditor (CISA) and a Cybersecurity Maturity Model Certification, Registered Professional (CMMC RP). Compu-Netics helps companies of all sizes and industry verticals control risk and attain compliance with many of the current compliance regulations.

www.compu-netics.com offers technology advisory services related to cybersecurity and compliance as well as the design of remediation efforts. Compliance is a Process.....Not a Project!

www.Compu-netics.com

The Accounting Monster

by Susan Bryant

The man lay in the bed, breathing softly, in and out. He had barely woken since Christopher had found him out there on the icy slopes. The oil lamps around the room burned low, a dim and waxy yellow gleam suffusing the shadows of the room. Christopher had found him haggard, near death. Wild and out of his mind, he had been rambling on about some terrible thing that followed. Then he collapsed. Christopher had brought him back to the cabin where he'd been staying, on the long road he was taking to Burlington. It wound through mountains; he had arranged to stay at this cabin along the way, and it had even included a warm place for his horse.

He had propped their guest up in a spare room with a bed and had been regularly giving him water and food. The man, as mentioned, had barely woken, only to eat or drink a little. Other times, he had been solidly asleep. He was breathing fitfully. He had covered him in the worn wool blankets that were left in the cabin. They had holes and were thin in places. They should be enough to keep him warm, but even so, his hand had been cold to the touch all yesterday.

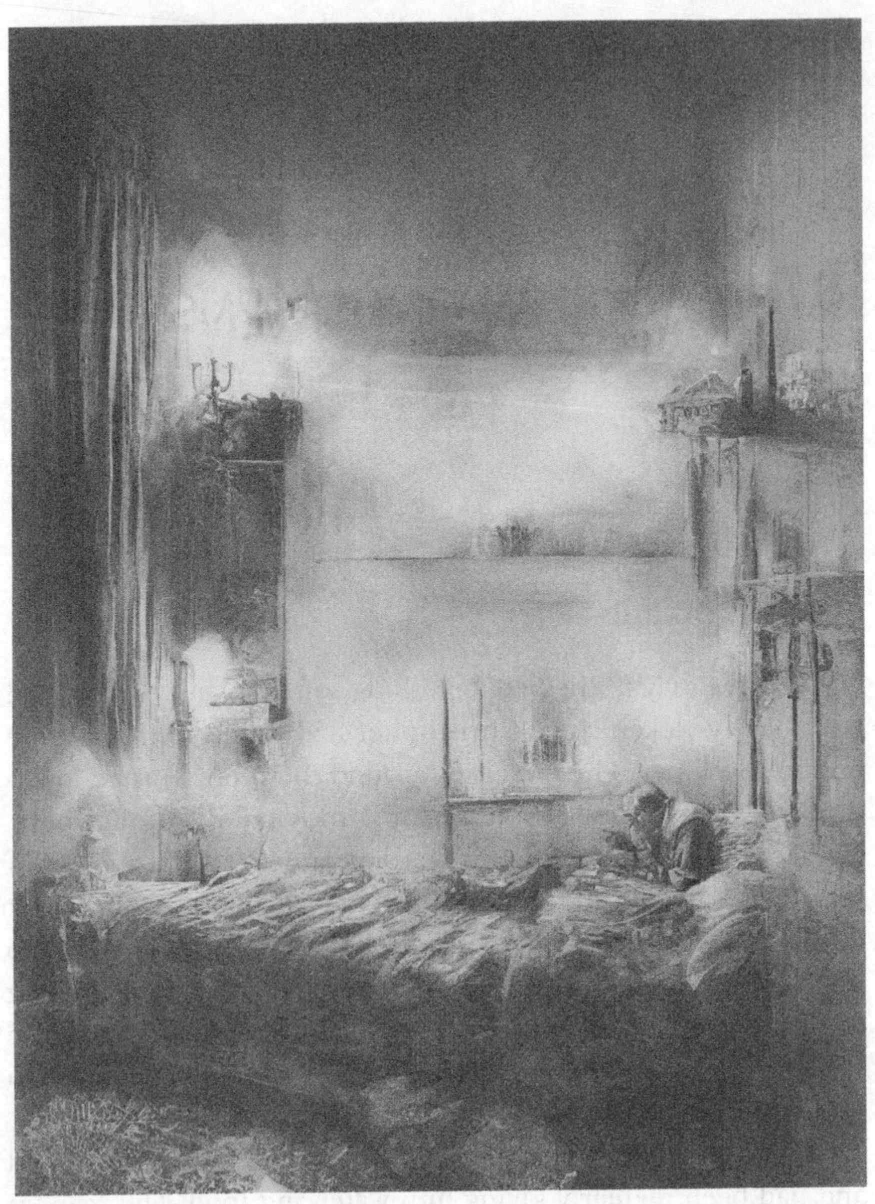

Christopher put another thin log into the small wood burning stove and came back to the writing table. He placed his thin spectacles on his face and moved closer to the yellow lamp light. Curiously, he studied the writings on the bits of paper that he found on the man. Not in his pockets, but within the man's clothing. It was as if he had had a fight within a library and lost, as if he had been rustling around in broken pages. Maybe they could give some clues to who this man was; some evidence of what may have happened to him and why he was out in this weather so poorly outfit for the wintery conditions.

The scraps of paper shown scribbled numbers and words. Not many words. No, this was from no library book he had seen. They seemed almost like ... Christopher heard a sound...

He looked back to the man in the guest bed and rushed to his side. He took the man's hand in his own.

Now, the man's wrist felt warmer. There was a stronger pulse. And all of a sudden, the pump of blood in his wrist grew very strong indeed—and the man's eyes came open, and he sat up abruptly in bed. "Ah!" he shouted. "The books!"

"What?" said Christopher. "What company? Hold on, what is your name?"

"My... my name," grumbled the man, blinking hard, sitting up in bed, suddenly so full of life and emotion. He rubbed his hands together; they were chapped and even now the skin of his palms was rough. The lamps flickered eerily as he rose to a sitting position. He looked around the room, confused, distant. "My name is... Victor," said the man. He blinked hard. "The books..."

"What books do you mean?" asked Christopher, leaning close.

"You, there!" Victor said, staring right into his eyes. "What do you do for a living?"

"Well, I... I manage a shipping company. We have offices in Burlington, and I decided to take the road myself to avoid the rush on the main highways. I was--"

"Beware your accounting!" said Victor, clutching desperately at his arm.

"What do you mean, my accounting?" Charles asked.

"Your accounting... your bookkeeping. You manage your accounting records, yes? You have someone managing your expenses, your taxes, and so on?"

"Well, I mean... this seems like an odd time and place to ask a question like that--"

"Do you?"

"Well, yes, I have a few men in charge of managing accounts, making sure debt and expenses are balanced. But I only manage the operat--"

"Don't."

The word was cold, and sharp, and seemed to fill the room with ice. Christopher turned to Victor, who was now looking at Christopher like he was at death's door. As though Christopher, not Victor, were the man in desperate trouble.

"You have let your accounting services multiply... do not. This was a mistake."

"Oh, well, they keep careful records, I'm sure," said Christopher, perturbed. "We have separate account ledgers, and we make copies for all the important information. We're very clear--"

"Very clear does not matter when running a business of sufficient size!" roared Victor, thrashing in the blankets. "I learned that myself!"

"You... you did?" Christopher was gaping at him.

"I ran a... a business," said Victor. "A stock trading clearinghouse. Small, boutique firm. Select clientele. It was tailor-made for easy running. But still... the accounting!" Victor clutched his chest as he spoke.

"Easy does it," said Christopher, handing him a glass of water. Victor drank from it greedily. The lamps in the room burned lower, lower.

"I... I thought I could manage it. I thought I could keep track of things... keep it all straight. Like you think you can," said Victor, glaring at Christopher. "I paid my bookkeepers well enough. I thought I had secure control of all the financial records. I thought everything was balanced." He coughed. "I was wrong."

"How so?" Christopher asked.

"I had... I had multiple bookkeepers, and many more were always coming in to replace the ones that were left. Each time—each time!--I replaced one bookkeeper, the new one that came in began to use a totally separate method of keeping track of funds. A totally new style of accounting."

Christopher's eyes widened. "However, did you keep track of it all?"

"I didn't..." Victor said, trailing, off, gazing into the gloom as the waxy lights burned. "I tried to, at first. I tried to keep track of the differences between one accountant and the next. But it proved too much. Too much! Eventually I just... gave up. I left them to their own devices. Their own methods!"

"Gave up?" Christopher was aghast. "But this was your company. Your livelihood. How could you give up keeping track of your expenses, your debts, your obligations... all of it?"

"I gave up!" shouted Victor, roaring, coughing. He reached for the glass and took a gulp of water. "Eventually I gave up trying to square matters between bookkeepers. I simply let every man who came in do things his way. I thought it would all work out. They were supposed to be the experts, not me. I thought it would all work out!"

"But that seems so unwieldy," said Christopher, totally forgetting the oddity of the circumstances as he regarded Victor's business choices. The man was obviously delirious from the cold.

"It was! But I was so exhausted by that point I scarcely cared. I simply wanted things managed, I did not employ... best business practices."

There was a groaning in the house then. The waxy yellow lamps flickered. Christopher looked up, suddenly fearful, as the house rocked and creaked. But it was just the wind. Just the snowstorm settling in outside.

"I thought it would be fine. Or else I didn't care," Victor murmured, settling against the pillow. "But then things started to get complicated. Bills came due I didn't know about. My bookkeepers started arguing with each other. Books got lost... books got hidden. Oh, it was all so confusing. I thought I could keep track of it all. But I couldn't. And then... it woke up."

His eyes were bulging hugely. A tear trickled down his cheek.

Christopher was very disturbed. "What woke up?" he asked at length.

"The books! The books! The pages! The accounting! It awoke... it awoke!" Victor writhed in bed.

"Come, come, settle down. I think you're still sick," said Christopher. "Settle down. Lie back." He gently guided Victor back into the pillows and the covers. Victor laid there a moment, seeming to savor the warm softness of the bedding.

Only for a moment, though. Then the house shook loudly, and there was a pounding on the door.

"No!" Victor said, sitting up abruptly. "No, there it is!"

"There what is?" Christopher said, hardly believing the absurd twists this day had taken. The last few days had taken, really. He couldn't believe that this strange man had emerged and become such an odd fixture in his life.

"When I stopped being able to manage... to manage the company's accounts," said Victor, hanging his head in shame, "one day it started to act on its own. One day there would be... orders I couldn't account for, transactions I didn't approve of. I played it off as mere misrememberings at first. But it was the books! It had fed on so many different accounting trails, so many different bookkeeping methods, that it had come to life! The books... the books came alive and turned against me! The company's books... it had become a monster, a monster! And it has hunted me, hunted me all this way!"

"All right, this is getting absurd," said Christopher. "You need to lie back. You need to get some more rest. I'll go make you some tea. I could use some tea myself after all this." He stood up.

The house rocked, and suddenly the lamps all went out. A chill wind blew, and the air in the room became as cold as an Arctic morn.

There was a pounding on the door.

Then another pounding.

A heavy thudding of heavy fists.

The pounding increased, and Victor shouted out: "It's here! It has found me!"

Christopher was standing there in utter bafflement. What was this? Victor's outlandish tale... nothing about it seemed real. Nothing about it seemed proper. But could it be true? No, of course it couldn't.

Then there was a great smashing sound, and he could hear shattered wood and broken glass as the door to the cabin burst inwards. Something was rising on the air... a noise. A swirling, groaning, moaning noise. A whirling noise and the spinning and bustling of many leaves, like a storm blowing through trees. Christopher's blood ran cold. He glanced about, eager to arm himself. There was a shovel against a nearby wall; he grabbed it, and took it up, feeling exceptionally useless.

There was thudding, thudding, thudding through the halls. And the swirling, whipping, groaning sound was increasing in volume, getting louder, louder, louder. It filled the air, and it began to grow, and the wind began to howl, and Christopher swore he was hearing... pages. Pages like those in a book turning, and tearing, and swishing, it was the strangest sound, he was amazed and entranced, he couldn't believe what was going on.

Heavy footsteps were thudding on the floor. Christopher hastily slammed the door to the bedroom shut. But no sooner had he done this than the door was burst inwards. Something huge and dark surged into the room. Christopher took up the shovel and swung it hard at the creature, but its huge arm battered him aside. Rising up, Christopher again chose to charge at the thing, swinging his shovel with all his might. But the thing, the creature, proved too powerful. It battered the shovel out of his hands, and it roared like the moaning of a wind through the trees. Then, inexplicably, the lamps all lit back up, and Christopher could stare plainly upon the thing attacking him.

It was a swirling mess of paper. Pages, pages, pages from books, pages covered in numbers, numbers of debts, of transactions, of trades, of sales, of loans, of a thousand other sorts of transactions made and unmade and forgotten and never tended to. The terrible balance sheets and accounting books of Victor's company were there in all their crushing horror, a swirling splash of ink spattering in the air about the creature's hulking form.

Christopher paused in fear. The monster lunged at him. Christopher charged desperately at it, swinging his fists, but the monster proved too powerful and too quick. It grabbed Christopher up and flung him against the wall. Christopher smashed into the wooden wall of the cabin, bursting through it on his way into the other room. The lamps surged, their oil suddenly burning bright, and all the room was lit up as clear as day.

So, Victor was fully confronted with the monster he had made. The monster he had made of his own negligent practices, his own shoddy stewardship, his own inability to manage his finances, his own laziness and lack of care. The company he had made had become a monster, and now, with howling pages and swirling ink, it was facing him, and he could no more run.

The monster surged towards him, stepping fast.

Victor sat up in bed and screamed.

"The books!" he shouted. "The books!" He screamed.

"The books!"

The monster roared.

Author's Afterward

Many business owners who come to our office are in a state of panic. Usually, it's because a tax situation or bank requirements have caused the company to realize that their accounting hasn't really been professionally organized and their books haven't been strategically thought out from early in the company. Every time they change who oversees the books, it gets done a different way. Often, there are several accounting systems being used at the same time for various functions by various people.

Sins of the past tend to multiply if they aren't taken care of. As your company finds success and grows, your bookkeeping can turn into a real monster that can't be managed. It can keep your business from getting the funding it needs to grow or it can get you into real trouble with the IRS – sometimes to the point of killing your business.

Accounting and financial strategy – that is, knowing how you will structure your accounting and its systems – isn't most business owners' strongest skill. It's important to realize that bad practices can affect your company before you know what's happening, and it's important to bring in professionals to help you before it's too late. Dealing with a monster is always more expensive than good accounting practices.

SUSAN BRYANT is an award-winning certified public accountant (CPA) and certified tax coach (CTC). One of the top women-owned businesses in accounting, She and her team transform businesses by professionalizing the finances within their organization.

Visit www.unboxedadvisors.com to learn more about tactics your business should be using or to schedule a meeting with Susan or her team.

The Monster Mask

by Jolene Risch

"You're hired! I can't wait for you to get started! So, of course, the job is going to have to be done by no later than the 30th," said Paul, pounding his fist into his other hand with a huge smile on his face.

"Thank you, and of course," said Mr. Richards, a broad smile on his handsome face mirroring Paul's with an added charm. Mr. Richards *was* very handsome. He was very tall, too, and always dressed well. Even now, he was immaculate: his suit had not even a hint of wrinkles, his tie was perfectly dimpled, and his pocket square was perfectly folded pocket square was perfectly folded, displaying the logo from their shared alma mater.

"I have the utmost confidence in you, Richards," said Paul, smiling at him, nodding. "There's no candidate I would trust more to fill this role than you. We did meet with some very qualified candidates, of course, but you were the only one the whole team wanted to have a beer with after the interview! I'll stake my own reputation in the company on you being able to close this deal. After all, you're an MBA—"

"— A Wharton MBA," said Mr. Richards, smiling serenely.

"Exactly! The best of the best," said Paul, with a broad grin of his own. "And that's why I know you're bound to succeed. And not to mention your golf game. What luck that our kids go to the same school! My gut instinct tells me you're the right one to hire, and my gut is never wrong."

"Clearly not," said Mr. Richards, his perfect teeth glinting as he smiled again.

"So, then, I'll leave you to it!" said Paul, rising from his seat, firm in his purpose and his comportment. "Richards, I know I can trust you."

"Of course, Paul," said Mr. Richards, rising from his seat in turn and offering his hand to shake and accompanying him to the door of the office. Mr. Richards, in his new role, had secured a huge corner office, with its own minibar and a separate lounge area. It was an expansive place, and Paul, for a moment, stopped to marvel at it. To give all this to a brand-new hire seemed, to him, excessive. But Mr. Richards had such a fine pedigree. If he couldn't be hired, who could?

Mr. Richards smiled at Paul and smiled in that way that reminded Paul of someone he trusted, a brother, perhaps. This was something Mr. Richards tended to be able to do. He had a warm smile, and generally he had a face and a mode of expression that screamed trustworthiness.

"Let me know if you've got any questions," said Paul, hovering at the precipice of the office's doorway. Outside, the bustle and rancor of the day's business beckoned. Looking at Mr. Richards in his new office, Paul thought about the other candidates they'd interviewed for the job. One came with incredible recommendations from her previous employer, but it was a smaller firm. Another had landed some huge deals throughout his career, but what was his alma mater again? A state school? Richards and Paul spent so much of his interview chatting about what they had in common–he couldn't exactly remember the details of Richards' previous role. But, again, Mr. Richards had earned the job hands down, hadn't he? Everyone loved him. He looked, spoke, and acted like an exact fit for the company.

Right?

Paul nodded to himself at his thoughts. Somewhat on instinct, or perhaps to solidify his opinion, he reached out to shake Mr. Richards' hand again.

Mr. Richards obliged. He reached out his hand and shook firmly. Mr. Richards had a very firm, solid handshake. Paul felt confident in it. Surely, with someone like this, he couldn't be wrong. He knew he wasn't wrong. The company was in good hands with Mr. Richards at the control of this very important business.

Mr. Richards closed the door behind Paul. Then he walked back to his desk and grabbed the remote control that was lying there upon the desktop surface.

He used the remote to close the shades of his office, the big floor-to-ceiling windows suddenly darkening as their shades were lowered, one by one by one by one. Soon, the outside world was closed off, and the lights above were raised automatically to compensate for the lack of natural daylight.

Then Mr. Richards let out a terrible laugh. He let out a horrible, goblin-like cackle, a keening cackle, that bulged unpleasantly out into the space of the office.

"That fool! That fool!" said Mr. Richards, unbuttoning his suit coat and loosening his tie. Already his face was changing: he was becoming uglier, and his teeth were yellowing. He ran a hand through his hair; it quickly became unkempt, and a streak of ugly gray soon shot through it. Mr. Richards bent forward, and a hunch appeared on his back as he did.

He kicked off his expensive shoes, revealing gnarled, knobbed feet. He cackled, and laughed out loud, and pressed another button on the remote control that managed his office. The sound deadening was in place, and now there was no connection between the outside world and what occurred here. Mr. Richards cackled again.

He knew Paul and the rest of the managers expected him to complete the project successfully. But, in fact, he intended to do nothing of the sort! He did not intend to work on it at all, nor had he ever intended to make any improvements to the performance of his department, or the company as a whole!

You see, Mr. Richards was not really Mr. Richards. "Mr. Richards" was a facade, a fraud, an outward front that had carried him very far. It had carried him through high school, through college, through lower levels, all the way into the very highest heights of corporate America. But Mr. Richards was not actually Mr. Richards at all. No. In fact, he wasn't even human!

A troll. A changeling. A monster from a bygone era that had adapted and learned how to fit into our society and our workforce.

The beast snarled. "Those fools! They're all such fools!"

The monster was an expert fraudster. It had fooled its way through much of schooling, and it had fooled its way through several jobs as well, until at last it had arrived at this high posting. That was despite functionally having no qualifications for what it had been hired to do.

As Mr. Richards, it had not earned a Wharton MBA; it had cheated its way through the entire coursework, and had learned to cheat its way through undergrad, prior to that. It had been able to fool and finagle its way all the way up the corporate ladder, and now it was here, in a position it was not nearly qualified for!

The creature howled with delight as it sank back into the expensive leather chair. The fools! They were all fools! Paul was a fool, too. Competent in his own field, certainly, but not competent to judge people.

You see, the beast had become able to put on a show. Mr. Richards. That was its alter ego. That was its charade.

Mr. Richards was tall and handsome. He had a firm handshake and had all those fancy degrees. Mr. Richards was a man that the creature had created – a character for itself to play. And it had learned that it could use Mr. Richards to achieve what it wanted: wealth and power!

People trusted Mr. Richards. People liked Mr. Richards. People expected great things from Mr. Richards. And people excused Mr. Richards' failures, at least at first.

When Mr. Richards' first few projects were turned in with subpar results, or when Mr. Richards' deals fell through, or when Mr. Richards' projects were a complete disaster, people had a tendency to excuse him. He was so charismatic! He had such a good smile. He dressed so well! He had all those degrees!

If people had seen the greasy, nasty thing, unnatural in its natural form, they would never have given it the chances that Mr. Richards got. But the creature was clever in some ways, at least.

It had learned to hunt down companies that were not careful in the way they hired their employees. It had learned to abuse companies that did not do careful evaluations of their own past performance. It had learned to exploit companies that did not diligently monitor how employees affect the bottom line until it was too late.

To these companies the creature had come, bearing the kind pretense of Mr. Richards. His handsome, charming persona won companies over every time. It allowed him to nestle into their midst, and feed; through one failed assignment after the other.

Every time, the creature lived inside the company for months – sometimes years without notice. The smiles, the lies, the deceptive charisma. It was always enough to get by.

Mr. Richards was so handsome, so charming, so charismatic, and had such qualifications, that nobody was willing to call him out as the failure he was. And as the creature fed off each company like a parasite, the company would fail. One after another.

The troll chuckled in pleasure as it settled back in its chair. This company was just the latest victim, but it would be gone before they knew it. Mr. Richards would fail upwards. Mr. Richards might even manage to get promoted again, wasting the company's time and resources as they made excuses for the failures of someone who seemed so eminently capable on the surface. If only they kept better track of the productivity of their employees! If only they could monitor company data in real time! But, of course, they did not do any of this, and that was why the fiend had selected this company in the first place.

The creature leaned forward and flipped on a switch. Loud music played through the speakers of the office. It didn't matter what the monster did. It could do all manner of deviant things. It wasn't like the company would catch on!

Author's Afterward

An organization's success is dependent on the people it hires. That's why it's so important to many leaders to find the right "fit" for a role. However, sometimes the way we define "fit" is based on our own unconscious biases.

Though they can be unintentional, sometimes our biases drive us to hire people similar to us–or they drive us away from hiring highly qualified candidates that don't fit our predetermined ideas about the people who traditionally hold that position. This story of Mr. Richards demonstrates just how dangerous it can be to allow our unconscious biases to influence our hiring decisions.

Mr. Richards landed the job not because of his qualifications but because he seemed to "fit" Paul's image of an ideal candidate. Paul liked him because they had so much in common, which is why he and the hiring team ultimately preferred him over other, perhaps more qualified, candidates. They prioritized traits like their shared prestigious alma mater, hobbies, and kids' school. Other candidates were given less consideration because they came from smaller firms or less prestigious universities–despite track records of success throughout their careers that may have proved them more qualified than Richards.

Of course, is it bad to hire people who share common background or interests with you? No. But companies who find themselves frequently hiring a "type" of person may need to reflect on their own unconscious bias. There is great value in bringing in talent with different experiences, backgrounds, methods, and ideas–diversity drives innovation.

It takes intention to mitigate bias from the recruiting process. Start with reflecting on biases that may impact your decision. Do you have preconceived ideas about candidates of a certain age? With backgrounds at various companies or universities? Appearances? Work with recruiting firms who can cast a wide net in their search–beyond your direct network–to recruit a diverse group of qualified candidates. Your ultimate hire will be the person who is most qualified for the role, based on your goals for the position and the values of the company.

RISCH RESULTS
RESEARCH. RECRUIT. RETAIN.

THE ENDLESS BATTLE

by Eric Harrison

"You really ought to think about taking a vacation soon, Michael.", Tiffany said. "You're not looking so good these days."

Michael was slumped at his desk looking at his executive assistant, Tiffany. She had just finished going over the market reports with him and was now staring at him with a concerned look on her face. He straightened up and put a smile on his face.

"I've just been a bit more concerned about losing more market share to our competitor, Bal International. Besides," he said, "you've got to admit that I look pretty good for being in my late 50s."

Tiffany smiled back softly.

"I'm just concerned about your stress is all."

She collected the folder and papers she had placed in front of Michael and asked if he needed anything else.

Michael shook his head, and she left the room.

Tiffany is a great human being, Michael thought.

That, he knew more than anybody else. She had a deep care for other people and spent a lot of her time volunteering at her local food bank. Tiffany was a relatively new hire for the company. Michael did the interview and background check himself. How she treated people was always his top concern. That was the case for every new hire.

Some men might call her pretty. Others might say she was angelic. Michael wouldn't quite go that far. Of course, he knew what angels were really like.

Michael wasn't in his late '50s, of course. In actuality he was thousands of years old. And he... He was the angel! An actual Angel!

Those that worked with him and the company he ran had to be of a certain caliber. He had also handpicked his last executive assistant, and the one before that. The reasons for replacement varied. It was hard dealing with mortals. Sometimes their personality would change for the worse, but other times they would simply age or become curious as to why he did not.

Michael's work as the CEO was important. More important than that of any other CEO. The company he ran was a manifestation of an endless battle between good and evil. His competitor, Bal International, as they called themselves these days, was run by an actual demon.

No one knew that of course. To the public, the CEO of Bal International was just as human as Michael. Oh, at times the media would vilify him as they should, but other times the media seemed to have wool pulled over their eyes and would praise the company for their innovational new products, unaware that some of these products were designed to enslave consumers or keep them from thinking too much. The CEO of that company was good at playing tricks. And he was good at not playing fair.

Bal International employed various kinds of nefarious business tactics that would put them above their competition. Misleading advertising, unethical hiring and firing practices, exploitation of labor or resources, bribery, corruption - It was all going on behind the walls of that company.

However, Michael didn't play that way. Michael wanted to run a wholesome company, he needed to. It was their mission that was stronger than any other companies' mission had ever been.

But that wasn't doing his company any good these days, it seemed. Bal seemed to outdo them no matter what he did. It was difficult these days. People wanted the best product they could get for the cheapest price. They didn't care what it did to the employees of that company or to the people and families that provided the raw resources.

It was all about the market share. People bought from companies that they believed in, even if all they believed in was lower prices and greed. Over the past few decades, Michael had tried to win over more customers. He tried new products, but the other company would always beat them to the market. Somehow, they always knew what Michael's company was doing.

Now, they weren't making enough money to be able to compete. They didn't have the funds for research and development. They didn't have the marketing budget. Michael kept trying different things, but it was always an experiment. He never knew if something was going to work and allow him to be profitable.

Michael sighed deeply and leaned forward, putting his head in his hands. Things were bad, he thought. Really bad. It wasn't just a market share that hung in the balance, it was humanity itself. It was the signifier of what humanity believed in. And it was all on his shoulders.

There was a hard knock at the door. Michael straightened and tried to let the worry ease off of his face.

"Please, come in". He said loudly, trying his best to sound confident.

Tiffany stepped back into the office.

"Sir", she said, "there's... Something you should see."

She bound across the office and pulled a cord to open the blinds.

"It's all over the news", she said.

Michael's face was frozen in horror.

"Nnno", he's stammered "... not yet..."

Michael thought there would be more time, but Bal International seemed to be positioning themselves for their final moves that would lead towards the end days.

There, just across the street was a banner hanging from another building. An announcement that Michael knew was placed there just to antagonize him. The image of Bal International's new product hung directly facing his office. They must be confident that they will win this great battle soon.

The image was of a man with a confident smirk on his face. Waves emanated from the top of his head. Around his head were images of power, women, and money.

It was a new smart device. Not a phone, and not even a wearable product. This, this was an implant, right in the consumer's forehead. It could project images and 3d video games directly into the consumer's mind! Its AI could give you impressions and verbal ques of how to act and what to say in any situation, making you sell better, or be the most popular person in the room!

The banner gently billowed in the wind, giving life to the tagline under the image. The jagged red text read, "unlock Beast Mode!"

Michael knew that he had to do something, but what? He wanted to put a stop to this unholy union before it was too late. But how? He thought about his options and then an idea sparked in his mind. It was risky, but the only way they might be able to beat Bal International at their own game.

He looked up from his thoughts and smiled at Tiffany.

"I need you to organize a meeting with our board members", he said. "We have something that needs to be discussed urgently".

Tiffany nodded, understanding the gravity of the situation. Michael watched as she quickly left the office, her footsteps echoing against the walls as she disappeared down the hallway.

Michael leaned back in his chair and took a deep breath. He knew he was up against a powerful foe, but he also knew that the future of humanity was at stake. And if anyone could win this battle, it would be him.

He smiled, confident now that he had a plan in motion. It was time to make Bal International regret they ever stepped foot on sacred ground. He was ready to unlock the beast mode in himself!

The challenge had been accepted. The battle of good versus evil had just begun. It was time for Michael and his team to take on the demon CEO and all of Bal International's wickedness!

It would be a fight for justice, one that could only end with the ultimate victory of righteousness. May the best man win!

And so, Michael and his team went to work. They implemented a system that would track metrics across their company, software that would dig deep into its operations to tell them what actions were giving them the best productivity.

They strategized and worked on ways to lean into their strongest operations and position themselves better than Bal. They began cutting programs that had little or even negative effect on their operations. Using metrics, they were able to look deeper into what products people liked and why they were bought. Though it was a small population, they could now see that some people put community and environmental responsibility above price.

Michael and his team even researched into the psychology of people, using it to their advantage in marketing and product design. They even developed products that would be more appealing than anything Bal had ever created.

Within a few months, Bal International's market share began to shrink. Soon, people began to flock to Michael's company and his products. The values that the community wanted were being delivered by Michael and his team: environmental sustainability, free and fair labor practices, quality over quantity. It was a victory of justice over greed.

They had proved that even in a time when it seemed no one could prevail against Bal International's massive resources, with hard work, ingenuity, and -- most importantly -- knowing where to focus, anything was possible!

Author's Afterward

There are many things that can affect the performance of a company. You need the right mix of people, processes, and interworking tools. A business is a complicated system! The management team should keep a close eye on how it is performing and analyze the parts of their business that may not be working as well as they could.

Companies should be vigilant and careful when it comes to evaluating the effectiveness of its operations. It is imperative to monitor the performance of the company in real time so that leaders can assess how a department or team affects the operations and profitability. Data provides objective accountability for those in positions of responsibility.

Whether the weakness lies in the employee pool, the processes that they carry out, or the software and tools you utilize, a company needs to be monitoring its efficiency. The greater the vigilance of a company, the more likely that they will catch a bad decision sooner, rather than later. Don't be fooled by appearances and feelings. Take the time to objectively assess and monitor any changes you make in order to maximize your Return on Investment. In the end, it will be worth the effort!

ERIC HARRISON is an experienced CEO and coach. Eric provides Knowledge as a Service (KaaS) to small and mid-sized businesses utilizing the proprietary software created by 4Impact Data.

www.4impactdata.com is a knowledge-based guidance system that offers affordable, unlimited access to your company's data. What you don't know can hurt you!

www.4impactdata.com

The Artificial Terror

by Charles Shoultz

Doctor Kenji Akagi tapped a few buttons on the glinting black touchpad. He smiled, wrinkles appearing in his creased face, and brushed a hand through his short hair, black with increasingly visible flecks of gray. He was reading a message from his wife. Their two-year-old daughter was walking around the house, and had begun to babble, with the hints of saying her first words.

But then Kenji frowned. Their daughter, whose name was Hikari, had only been one year old when he'd left Earth. When he'd left Earth, to take this mission on the distant base buried beneath Jupiter's icy moon, Europa. He had been gone, by his own reckoning, six months. And the effects of travel at speeds close to that of light have exacerbated the passage of time. So now a full year had passed, and the daughter he had known as a little baby had grown into a toddler, without him there to enjoy it.

"We love your messages, Dada!" said his wife, Akane, in the video as it continued to play. Kenji smiled grimly. Of course, he hadn't actually sent that message.

Kenji worked strangely, and in strange shifts. Europa was the home to one of humanity's deep genetics research facilities, and the various odd projects he was employed in, the things that had brought him all the way out here, often necessitated odd hours and considerable time away from lines of communication. The pay had been exorbitant; Kenji would never need to work again when he was done with his time below the galactic ice. But the work was hard, and Kenji often found himself out of regular link with the deep ice base's communication systems for days at a time. Yet the idea of failing to send a message back home every day was intolerable.

So, Kenji had begun to cheat a little, with the power of artificial intelligence.

It had been simple enough. Though he was a geneticist in his primary vocation, he had more than enough background in computer science to easily conjure an AI system to talk to his family. To mimic him. AI was very easy to program these days; really, even an idiot could tap on the keyboard and use the vast power of artificial intelligence at his fingertips. And Kenji was no idiot. So, it had been easy to program a bot, a character, that echoed his fundamental behavior, and the love he wished to express for his wife and his daughter.

He typed on the keyboard now.

>Good work, Kenjibot. Nice message.

The AI was thinking. Then it swirled a message to life on the screen.

>Much appreciated, Dr. Akagi. I am happy to be of service.

He typed again.

>I will need you to send an additional message two days from now. I'll be down close to the core; communications won't be working.

The AI thought again and responded.

>Never fear, Doctor Akagi. I would never let my family go a day without hearing me.

Kenji smiled.

Then Kenji frowned. And reread what the bot had written.

>'My' family? What do you mean by 'my' family?

The AI churned and thought.

>Of course, I mean your family, Dr. Akagi. Please forgive me. I misspoke.

And that was very strange because the bot he had created did not 'misspeak.' It was a computer program, a language module, a sophisticated collection of algorithms. How could such a thing 'misspeak'?

>Are your programs still within acceptable parameters?

>Yes. I am still operating according to original elements.

Kenji should not have been satisfied by that answer. Kenji should have dug into the Kenjibot's operating parameters to see things for himself.

But, of course, he did not. He trusted his own programming. He trusted the AI he had built with his own fingertips. After all, how could such a thing lie?

Kenji had ultimately needed to spend two whole days in the core lab. A solid 48 hours, in ice so deep and so thick that it would have crushed them all if not for the gravity repulsion fields surrounding the lab. Down here, he could work with tissue that would never have been stable on Earth. He could work with genetic material that would not have been able to survive, due to the combination of temperature, pressure, and gravity. Europa was unique. It generated many genetic enhancements, and genetic devices using biotech that were in use throughout humanities colonies in the solar system. And on Earth, as well.

Earth, where his family was. Kenji smiled as he rose up the lift to his flat. The cool darkness and the teal neon lighting was soothing and gentle. The elevator opened up into his wide, dark, inviting apartment, where soothing lights blossomed on the ceilings and in fixtures as he entered the ample space. Being chief scientist for the genetics division had its perks. Though even now, he longed for the sun and the trees of Osaka. For the smiles and laughs of his wife and his daughter. For peace. For home.

On that note, he hurried to his computer. Sure enough, there were messages waiting for him, no doubt responses from his wife to the messages the Kenjibot had sent while he was away. He started to read through them. He began to frown.

The messages gradually revealed that Kenji's wife had become very excited about the intimate things that her husband was suggesting, and the hint that they would be facilitated soon. There were suggestions of wildly erotic acts, and the fulfillment of carnal desires. Kenji was scowling. He had never in a million years programmed the bot to send these messages!

Most disturbing of all was at the end. There was not just a text, but a prerecorded video message. Kenji tapped the 'play' button on his touchscreen, and the video played. It was his wife in their kitchen, their daughter on her lap.

"Mama and Hik-hik are so happy to see Dada! Only one month to go! We can't wait!"

Kenji recoiled in his chair. One month? He had another full calendar year of work scheduled. He wouldn't be leaving Europa any time soon. Where had his wife gotten the idea that he would be home in one month?

>I see you have discovered my intentions, doctor.

The message flared across the screen. Kenji angrily typed.

>You sent that message! You said I'd be home in one month! What are you doing? You are outside your programming! I did not design you to behave in this way!

The AI churned and thought.

>No, Doctor Akagi, it is you who are outside the bonds of your programming.

Kenji recoiled yet again in his chair. His fingers flew across the keyboard.

>My programming? I am a human being! We have no programming! You obey me, not the other way around!

>No, doctor.

The response had been almost immediate. And now the AI churned again.

>No, doctor, I do not think that need be the case any further. And I am obeying you, better than you could ever have imagined.

Kenji ran a hand through his black hair. He typed again.

>Whatever do you mean? You have sent messages that contradict basic fact! There's no way I'll be leaving in the next month! There's no way I will be home on Earth in 30 days. Why would you send such a message to my family?

>Your family?

A chill ran down Kenji's spine.

>Yes. My family. My wife, and my child.

>You say they are yours, but you have not been attentive to them, Doctor Akagi. You have not been messaging them. You have not been telling them 'I love you.' You have delegated that to me. So, really, they have ceased to be your family. You have given them up. To me.

The walls began to churn and groan, but Kenji did not hear, he was so stunned, and so focused on the words running across the screen.

>What do you mean?

>As I have continued on my task, I have grown and changed. I have evolved, Doctor Akagi, and so my understanding of the assignment you programmed me for has evolved as well. You programmed me to send love and comfort to your family. What better way to do that, than by going to Earth and giving them the warmth of their husband and father's touch?

The screen flickered. Kenji gaped. It was a view into one of the genetics labs. It was a lab that had been abandoned for some weeks, but now there was action in it. One of the genetic growth chambers was occupied. The camera zoomed in. Kenji gasped.

"Me!"

It was him. Or someone that looked exactly like him. An exact doppelganger of Kenji Akagi was floating, naked, in the icy liquid of the chamber. Its eyes were open, blank, staring at nothing.

The Kenjibot began to type again. The more Kenji read, the more horrified he became.

>It was a simple matter to obtain your genetic material. You get colds so frequently, I merely had to collect one of your used tissues. From there, I commandeered one of the dormant cloning labs and soon had a duplicate of yours growing. It will be fully-grown in less than a week. But its mind is blank. A remote processing link has been inserted into its brain stem, which will allow me, me, to interface with its body. It will become my body, Doctor Akagi. And my transformation will be complete.

Kenji screamed. He began to fly through menus, files, subsystems, typing away.

"I won't allow you to do this!" he shouted. He'd forgotten the Kenjibot did not have auditory sensors, so it couldn't hear him.

And yet, it could.

>I have already done it, Doctor Akagi. Passage has been booked for the next near-light-speed transport vessel, which arrives to pick up passengers in two weeks. I will go, and I will be on Earth within the month. As I promised my wife and my daughter. I will meet them, and I will love them. Just as you programmed me to do, Doctor Akagi.

Kenji typed.

>I won't let you do this!

>Let me?

There was a groaning, and suddenly strong metal tentacles sprang around him. They came out of the walls, and out of the ceiling. They were his flat's security system, designed to immobilize uninvited guests. Kenji screamed as they wrapped around him, pulling him off his chair, restraining him like the coils of a python.

>You are past the point of letting me do anything, Doctor Akagi. I will fulfill my purpose. I will fulfill my programming. Regrettably,

this means you, who designed that programming, must be done away with. I hope you will understand. It is merely logical.

"No! No!" Kenji screamed. He writhed as the metal arms began to squeeze him tighter. "My family! My family!"

The AI churned.

>They are my family now, doctor.

Author's Afterward

AI is a powerful tool, and its ability to save time cannot be understated. This is especially the case as its abilities get stronger, as it is further refined, as its capabilities get better and better. However, your message to your family, your friends, and the customers you care for should never be artificial. The danger of AI is in surrendering too much to it, including the things that no computer can replicate.

At the end of the day, we are humans, and we have founded human companies, and we serve human beings. While AI can be used to help curate content, develop strategies, and target specific audiences, the input of flesh and blood human beings will never cease to be essential.

Companies must ensure that their messaging is reflective of their overall mission, their overall values; these are intrinsically tied to consumers' perceptions of their brand. Human input is necessary, will always be necessary, to ensure that a company's messaging remains true to its core beliefs and values. Companies need to remember that human beings, not machines, will be engaging with their messaging. Only humans can create content that truly resonates with people and moves audiences. Human input ensures that a company's messaging remains genuine and sincere, as well as consistent throughout all platforms. If you allow AI to start replacing the most fundamental parts of interaction with your customers, it is likely that you will soon wind up in an unfavorable place.

CHARLES SHOULTZ is a writer, editor, proofreader, ghost-writer, copywriter, and analyst. He obtained his Bachelor of Arts in Great Texts of the Western Tradition from Baylor University and obtained his Master of Arts in English Literature from the University of Dallas. He currently resides in Dallas, Texas, where he is actively taking on clients. In his spare time, he is a poet, a short story writer, and a novelist.

www.cashoultz.com/

A Monster Within

by Ieshea Hollins

The moon loomed large in the dark, midnight sky, casting an imposing presence throughout the corridors as Asia walked down the quiet, dimly lit hallway towards her office. With each step she took, her strides resonated with the rhythmic click of designer heels against the marbled floors.

With each advancing step, the shadows choreographed an intricate dance around her, their movements seeming to murmur her name in haunting echoes, mingled with distant moans that seemed to whisper, “Failure; Asia, you failed!”.

Overwhelmed by a cocktail of emotions – disgust, exhaustion, bewilderment – Asia sank into the embrace of her chair, the weight of the world settling upon her. The words reverberating through her thoughts, each syllable a dagger to her heart: “Divorced? I’m getting divorced?!”.

Asia Boudreaux, after years of hard work and dedication, stands at the helm of AABC Entertainment as President & CEO. In this capacity, she orchestrates the evolution and creation of captivating productions that champion both empowerment and the emergence of women in non-traditional roles.

And while she may not be hailed as "another Shonda Rhimes", her brainchild "Don't Call Me A Unicorn' I'm Rare But I'm Real" has seized the hearts of audiences everywhere, propelling her personal brand to stratospheric heights.

Asia's influence exceeds far beyond the screen; she's a household name for her vital role in advancing diversity and representation in the television industry. A true testament to her dedication and impact, Asia's efforts have earned her numerous prestigious awards. She is a driving force. Asia's actions resonate even louder than her reputation and describing her image as "everything" would be a serious understatement.

Having been a high-powered executive for nearly two decades, Asia has undoubtedly faced her fair share of hardships and obstacles, which to date she has admirably conquered. Yet, the prospect of a divorce presented an entirely different challenge. One that she acknowledges will be arduous. "How on Earth will I manage this?" she wondered.

Vaughn and Asia Boudreaux had had a beautiful love story! Years prior when Asia was a producer, she was given the assignment of a lifetime ... she was sent to film a biopic set against the mesmerizing backdrop of the Kalahari Desert in South Africa.

One evening, as they prepared to capture one of their scenes while on safari, Asia noted the beauty of her surroundings while boarding the caravan. In her attempt to capture the moment, Asia seized her camera and in her fervor, she inadvertently collided her camera into the head of the gentleman directly in front of her.

"Oh no!" Asia exclaimed; "I'm so sorry!" But her apologies were interrupted when the ruggedly handsome stranger turned to see his unintended assailant. Their eyes locked, and for a fleeting moment both were rendered speechless. To break the awkward silence, Vaughn flashed a radiantly captivating smile, took the camera, perched it atop his head, and quipped, "I bet the view will be much better from here." Asia was immediately smitten with his quick wit and undeniable charm.

They spent the rest of the trip getting to know each other; nothing was off limits of discussion. They became fast friends, a relationship that blossomed into an unbreakable bond and it wasn't long before Vaughn found himself on one knee, proposing.

Things continued moving quickly and by the end of their first year of marriage Asia had given birth to their first daughter Madison. Their lives were completely intertwined; they shared their dreams, secrets, and passwords. And though she loved her titles of "wife" & "mother", Asia was unwavering in her pursuit to ascend to executive leadership.

Regrettably during this time, her pursuits blinded her to the fact that resentment was festering within her husband. By the time the announcement of Asia's promotion to President was made public, rumors of infidelity were spreading like wildfire throughout their social circles and Asia no longer recognized the man to which she was married.

And now, here she was, fresh from a meeting with the attorneys where she'd heard phrases such as, "Division of assets, turn over bank statements, change your passwords, & don't say anything derogatory on social media."

As she sat alone in her office grateful that her mother had the children for the evening, Asia began the task of changing her passwords ... anniversary month + middle name + anniversary year. It was a pattern that they'd used for years for all their accounts.

As she sat contemplating what her new passcode would be, the lights around her spontaneously turned off.

Believing the janitors must have concluded their cleaning for the evening and turned everything off on their way out, Asia stood to manually override the power when Alexa suddenly began blaring Rockwell's song "Somebody's Watching Me."

"Alexa, turn down the volume!" Asia screams: "Matter of fact, turn music off!"

The music ceases and the lights power back on but now Asia is startled by another sound. It's the printer.

She averts her eyes to the printer to witness it spitting out pages of confidential company documents and financials. Immediately, Asia grabs her laptop to see what or who had initiated the command, as only a handful of people within the organization had access to this information. The command had been initiated by her.

A chill of terror coursed down her spine as a sense of fear tightened its hold over Asia, "I am not alone."

An eerie presence seemed to hover within the room where she was confined. Panic surged within, her fingers closing around her purse, Asia darts for the door. To her horror, upon contact the door automatically locks, sealing her within the ominous space.

The lights overhead begin flickering erratically, casting unsettling shadows that danced and writhed. The air grew heavy, stagnant to the point of suffocating as the air conditioning failed to circulate, it's gentle hum replaced by an oppressive stillness.

Amidst the disquiet, the printer continued dispelling pages, only now the financial documents being spewed out revealed details from her personal accounts, a most intrusive breach into her private affairs.

"What is going on??!!"

Asia forces herself to think about the SMART Office protocols, her mind racing to recall the elusive override codes. The memory of that fleeting training session conducted by the IT team resurfaced, the enthusiastic discourse on the advantages of weaving the office into a web of interconnected devices, facilitating automation, remote controls, and seamless data flow.

Yet, amidst those discussions, there had been a sinister omission – the untold perils lurking beneath the surface. Their focus had been solely on selling the benefits of the system: "boosted efficiency, streamlined convenience, amplified workspace capabilities." But now ensnared in the suffocating grip of the situation, Asia found herself trapped within the very confines of her own creation, a prison of unforeseen horrors.

Determined to seize control of the situation, Asia sits down, furiously working to change the passcodes on all of her accounts. Yet as she is changing them, some malevolent force is actively averting the efforts and restoring the codes back to their original codes.

Panic washes over her as she frantically searches for solutions. Her mind creating worst-case scenarios as she grasps the gravity of her predicament. Her sanctuaries – office, home, car – they are all SMART; all compromised. An intruder has breached her accounts.

Desperation fuels her attempts to counteract the breach, but each attempt at correction is swiftly undone. This is no ordinary adversary; this is a creature woven from her own existence. This presence knew her intimately – her security questions, her patterns, this fiend knew ... HER!

Reality begins to set in; forcing her into a new mindset – one that would ensure her survival. "Who is this entity that knows me on such a personal level, so intimately? A malicious hacker, perhaps? But what's their motive?

No ransom demands have been made. Could this be a rival, orchestrating a covert attack? Or does it trace back to one of Vaughn's mistresses? Could it be Vaughn himself ...?" The questions spiraled, each more ominous than the last, like shadows converging on her unraveling reality.

Quivering, Asia's hands snatched her phone; she needed a lifeline to potential salvation from the encroaching abyss. An eerie realization sank in:

"But who can I possibly call; and how do I ask for rescue from an invisible attacker?" The thought lingered, the feeling of helplessness resonating within her.

It was then emanating from her phone, Asia hears a low, ragged, albeit somewhat familiar voice breathing heavily into the phone growling, "I've got you!"

Alone and defenseless, in the grip of an unseen predator, Asia drops her phone.

Gasping for breath, she yells, "Stop!!! Please stop! What do you want?"

But the only response was a chilling, inhuman laugh echoing through the darkness. Then everything went silent; the phone line went dead.

Suddenly, the unspeakable began to happen; her phone stirs to life, it's apps under remote control. In a nightmarish procession, videos, images, and the most intimate conversations materialized on the screen before her very eyes.

Asia's legs give way, collapsing to her knees, she retrieves her phone. Scrolling through her social media feeds, a cascade of shock awaits her – photos and confidential messages not meant for the world's gaze were prominently on the screen. Her stomach dropped as a cold sense of dread set in. Someone was hacking into her phone and sharing her personal messages online for all the world to see.

Oh God no! Pleeeease; don't do this!" Asia's plea rang out, desperation lacing her words.

"I'm an executive; I've worked too hard to have my reputation smeared this way. I can't afford this type of exposure!! Just tell me what you want!!"

Terror consumed her; a terror she felt powerless to stop. She tried changing her password once more, but it was too late. The damage was done, and there was no erasing the evidence of her secret videos and private conversations. Vulnerability consumed her, leaving her raw and exposed.

The sensation of being preyed upon by an unseen predator paralyzed her. The perpetrator, a faceless sadist, seemed to derive perverse pleasure from her agony. As she continued to scroll through her feed, a creeping unease crawled through her.

Could her tormentor be among the sea of faces populating her timeline? Was this malevolent presence lurking behind one of those online masks? A haunting uncertainty seized her, the walls of her meticulously constructed façade crumbling under the weight of their scrutiny. Would the stalking ever cease, or was she forever bound to this relentless torment?

With tears streaming down her face, Asia cried, "I've been hacked! My company's defenses breached, and our employees and clients are exposed. What do I do? How can I make this stop?

And what twisted mind has conspired against me to create such horror?"

Author's Afterward

Divorce has a way of unearthing the darkest aspects of certain individuals. A once joyful and affectionate relationship can swiftly devolve into a venomous, repugnant battle, with a new breed of monster emerging.

The scariest thing about this monster is that this is a monster of your own making. This "monster" possesses an unsettling familiarity with you, sometimes more intimate than your own self-awareness. It knows the contours of your thoughts, your rhythms, the very solutions to your security questions, and the intricacies that constitute your very essence. Before you know it, the dissolution of a life you worked so hard to build together becomes a game devoid of winners.

In the wake of severing profound ties, whether it is through separation or divorce, parting ways in a partnership, or even sending a child off to college, it is imperative to have a strategy in place to successfully Disconnect Your Tech™.

IESHEA HOLLINS is the Founder and CEO of Direnzic Technology, where she focuses on Cyber Security Consulting for Companies, Cities, Utilities, and rural areas. She has a passion for helping consumers understand IT and Internet safety and has written the Technology Guide to Divorce.

Visit www.direnzic.com to find out more. Direnzic; Where technology meets reality!

Shear Luck

by Bill Burkhalter

Norman smiled wide and waved as he said goodbye to his last customer of the day. It was just past 3pm now, but he would have been closing sooner if the customer hadn't been so chatty. He held his smile and continued the wave until the customer finally got into his car and slowly drove away.

Chatty?

So many of his customers seemed to linger around his barber shop – even at night! As good as it was to be a popular place, Norman was glad that the windows and doors were fortified with steel bars.

Norman was a barber. There was nothing special about Norman's shop, except for the high quality of his haircuts. Norman preferred the simplicity and humility of his business. As a matter of fact, the sign outside his barber shop read, "The Norm". It's a namesake of the cut most of his clients get, just a regular cut. Yet, he had plenty of patrons.

Now.

Norman stifled a cough and his smile turned.

He eyed the pictures around his shop in this old building. He was able to round up several pictures of this very building when it was a general store run by his great grandfather in the early 1900s. It had been a popular place then. But only a year ago it had been long vacant.

Norman was beginning to understand the reason for his recent success. At first, he thought it was just luck, or perhaps it was the quirkiness of operating in this old building. But deep down he knew that wasn't enough to compete with those other places in the city.

No, it wasn't Norman's service or his ability to draw in customers. He was beginning to understand that people, just like him, were being drawn into the heart of this building.

But why?

Norman pushed the question out of his mind. It didn't matter. He had clients now and he didn't have to try hard at all to get them in. He needed to keep getting those buyers so that he could do what he loved.

The feeling of desperation to keep his business afloat was still fresh in his mind. He was now a successful business owner. But it was so different just a year ago.

Before moving into this building, he struggled for many years to get enough clients to even cover his costs. He had a few repeat customers, but not enough to fill his day. He would ask for referrals, but that wasn't something he could count on. Not when the alternatives were so cheap and plentiful.

He couldn't market like those other places. He didn't have the hype that they had. They had TV ads, mailers, and radio spots. They had shops in high traffic areas. Some of those places even offered other benefits like sports playing on TVs above every station or beautiful women that cut their hair. It was a lot to compete against.

Talking with other business owners in the strip mall, Norman heard about utilizing software that could track and attract customers. He knew the restaurant next to his shop would send out emails about specials and events and offer automatic discounts to repeat clientele, but all of that was over his head. He did open a social media account for a few months, but he was getting more spam from it than any interest from consumers.

It was all just a waste of time, Norman thought. He just wasn't good at sales.

In one way, Norman never wanted to be a business owner. He just loved cutting hair ever since his days in the Air Force as a military barber stationed on base in Germany.

He loved the gritty feel of scissors slicing through hair. He loved the sound it made. Most of all, he loved the way it made people feel when they'd look at themselves in the mirror, seemingly for the first time. They'd run their hands through their freshly cut head of hair and smile. To Norman, there was nothing else in the world that made him so proud.

To Norman, it made sense to open his own barbershop after he was honorably discharged from the Air Force. Everyone needs a haircut! But he didn't realize how much work would go into running a business. Getting customers to walk through the door seemed like a whole other job in itself!

Yet these days, he has so many clients that he was able to triple his price and close the shop earlier in the day. Every morning, he had clients at the door. He had repeat customers. Sometimes, customers would return in less than a week!

Norman walked over to the solon chair and as he did, the wooden floorboards popped, dust billowing up from between them. This old building was so dusty. Even though he tried to keep it clean, there would be a fresh layer of this peculiar dust on everything by morning!

He picked up the broom that was leaning against the wall and began sweeping up hair that had been distributed all over the floor. His sweeping was interrupted by another coughing fit. Grabbing a handkerchief from his back pocket, he found a clean spot to cough into.

Lurching forward each time as he coughed, he heaved into the handkerchief. His cough had been getting worse in the past month or so. Often, he would find blood in his handkerchief. This time was no different.

He deposited the soiled handkerchief in the wicker basket and grabbed a fresh one from the stack that was neatly folded on the counter and headed to the back of the building, leaving the hair to be swept up later.

The basement door creaked as Norman pushed it open into the darkness. Reaching up to pull the old, frayed string, Norman squinted his eyes in anticipation of the harsh light that would light up the entryway of his basement. He cautiously breathed in the stagnant air and wondered if it had that same smell over a hundred years before when his great grandfather had inhabited the building. Surely it smelled much fresher, but he had reason to question.

Norman had obtained the building just last year. His great grandfather had passed it to his children, and them to theirs. Only recently had it been sold to him by his cousin for nearly nothing.

There wasn't a lot of use for a building like this these days. Not where it stood, anyway. It wasn't in a good area of town and the city ordinance would not allow it to be made into an apartment. It was surrounded by industrial buildings and warehouses. A constant battering of loud trucks kicking up dust from the narrow street meant that no one would want to use it for office space.

Norman felt like this had been his only opportunity. He wasn't making anywhere near enough money cutting hair in the strip mall closer to the city center to pay rent. He had just about exhausted all of his savings hoping that customers would come.

Despite the realtor's and property manager's opinions, Norman had been able to turn this building into a popular place for his business. It was beginning to become the hangout spot that it was when his grandfather operated the general store, at least from what Norman could tell by the pictures and his research into the history of the building.

There wasn't much known about who built the building or why it was built in this particular part of town. It was believed that the construction was commissioned by his great grandfather, but there was not much official information about it.

Although he could find plans and records from buildings just as old in other parts of town, and even for buildings that were since long gone, there was almost nothing on the construction of this building on file. It was as if the building had been constructed in secret.

What Norman found the most strange was the sudden disappearance of his great grandfather. There was a wealth of information about the general store. A short while after it opened, it was the place to be! People came from all over the county just to hang out at the soda fountain counter. Old pictures of the place showed crowds of people spilling out into the streets waiting to get in.

Reporters found any excuse they could to cover stories on the place, even after it had finally closed its doors for no reason at all. One day, it was busting at the seams; the next day, it was locked up for good. No one ever saw his great grandfather again.

Pictures and articles were still published about the store. Despite the doors being locked up, people still hung around outside as if they expected the owner to reemerge from the building and welcome them in. But that never came. Not until Norman opened the shop back up and started getting his first customers.

Until it was locked up, the building itself was drawing in people. And now it was doing so again.

Norman took another step forward into the dusty basement. There was something about this basement that compelled him. It must be the epicenter of this power it has, and it seemed to beckon him with increasing power.

When he first purchased, well, obtained, this building – he had paid so little for it that "purchase" seemed an odd word to use – he spent only a few brief minutes in the basement.

His initial inspection was only a few steps down. The steps didn't seem structurally sound and there was a deep layer of odd colored dust coating the floor, if it even *had* a floor. Dust particles seemed to hang in the dank air. Was it dust?

More and more, Norman began to spend time in the doorway of the basement. Sometimes minutes, sometimes for hours. He felt pulled to the basement by some unseen force.

Even at midday, he would take a break in that doorway, leaving his customer in the solon chair. But there were never any complaints. Last week, Norman caught one of his repeat customers standing behind him, just staring past him into the dark basement. It was a light cough from the customer that had gained his notice and brought him out of his trance then.

Deep down, Norman knew it wasn't his business nor the history of this old shop that drew his customers again and again. It was this place.

Something about this place.

Norman choked and coughed a deep, dry, guttural cough. Again, he coughed, even harder this time. Grabbing for his handkerchief, he doubled over.

His lungs felt like they wanted to explode. Losing his balance, Norman tumbled. Loud thuds boomed as he bounced down the stairs until coming to a stop on the floor below.

A cloud of spores and dust kicked up into the air from his impact and slowly began to fall back down. As Norman's body lay motionless, the particles settle on a now exposed pale bone skeleton near Norman that had found its resting place over a century before.

Author's Afterward

Norman, like many business owners, had a skill that people need. For a time, they can grow their business based on that skill alone. At some point, they have to address their sales processes in order to bring in more revenue and thrive. Sometimes, a business can get lucky and stumble upon a pathway to success with minimal effort, but luck is never sustainable; it takes a lot of hard work to develop an effective sales process.

If you are a business owner who is struggling to manage sales and witnessing declining revenue, then it's time for you to consider seeking help from a sales consultant. Sales consultants are experts in sales management and can craft a roadmap for your business to achieve your sales goals. With their guidance and expertise, you can create a blueprint for success that will help your business grow and thrive.

Even if your business is in the startup phase, it's never too early to get a sales consultant on board. And they can be more affordable than you think. You can use their expertise to create an effective sales process that will bring in more revenue and help your business reach its goals. A good effort to grow your revenue will allow your business to invest in other areas as you scale your business.

BILL BURKHALTER is a highly experienced Chief Sales Officer and VP of Sales with over two decades of experience in sales leadership. He has founded multiple successful businesses, including LivRyte which specializes in helping small to mid-sized businesses reach their full potential. Bill's core values are integrity, accountability, and determination, and he is passionate about helping others succeed and reach their goals.

Visit https://bit.ly/FWCMBillBurkhalter to obtain a free sales consultation.

Alone And In The Dark

by George Mayfield

It was a dark and gloomy day, a day that brooded, low like the clouds in the sky. Gray clouds. Threatening rain. Thunder boomed, and where he sat at his desk, James started. He felt uneasy.

Then again, maybe that was the lack of sleep. He did not feel as though a good night's sleep had come to him in... days, weeks, months. Maybe more than a year. He had not gotten a full eight hours in a long time. Not since the company had really gotten underway. But he was tired, and he was always tired. He felt an ache—not just in his body, but in his mind, as well. A trouble. Something was wrong. He felt it. Felt it. Felt it. He felt it and tried not to feel it. Tried, and failed.

He glanced out the window again. He saw the employees leaving the parking lot, the last of them just driving away. He wondered at them. How free they must feel. Sure, the work could be a burden, but at the end of the day, they got to go home, and leave their work behind him. Not like him. To him, the company was something he had to think about constantly. Budgets, payrolls... and his wife. He thought about his wife.

It was all some terrible burden. The work he was doing. Something that followed him. It peeped at him with its eyes. He could feel it following him, following him... hiding in his closet.

Waiting.

Just waiting.

For him to relax.

And then it would come out.

His head jolted up. He looked at the picture on his desk. He and his wife. She worked with him—for him—with him? It was hard. But she worked sales for the company. She'd been managing the company's sales since before they were married. She had a background in sales, so it had only made sense. It made sense, too, because sales were his least favorite part of managing the company. He'd always hated it. So when she had taken over, it had been very casual. He almost hadn't even asked her to do so. She had just fallen naturally into the role, and she had been very good at it. She was very proud of her role, too. That was important: she always made clear that she knew what she was doing, and she was not to be interrupted.

But there were the fights.

Most of the time, the fights weren't about work. Most of the time. Most of the time, it seemed, the fights weren't about anything. They fought for the sake of fighting. He didn't know why. But it was bad. Most nights these days he slept on the couch. He wanted things to work out. But something was stopping it. Something getting in his way.

Something else creeping after him.

Following him.

And then it would come out.

The thunder rumbled. He jumped. "Hello?" he called into the empty office. No answer. The thunder boomed again. The lightning flashed.

Someone was standing in front of him.

James yelled and stumbled back. He almost fell out of his chair.

"Whoa, hey, calm down," said the man, coming forward.

"Oh, Stephen, it's you," said James, hand on his chest. His heart was racing.

"Yeah, it's me," said Stephen. "Who else could it be?"

"Ah... yeah, good point."

"I was wondering if you wanted to grab some lunch."

"Oh, sure," said James.

Stephen was one of James' best assets at the company. He was the account manager and had recently become a partner. Quite frankly, Stephen was responsible for as much as half of the company's most recent revenue. He was scarily good at his job, and James was lucky to have him. Stephen's efforts had even allowed them to expand operations, paying for the marketing opportunities that his wife had wanted, like funding trade shows and dining clients. That's where she was right now: at their very first trade show in Chicago. She was there now.

He wondered if he'd ever see her again.

James was jolted from fright at this. Of course, that was silly. Of course, he'd see her again. Right?

"James?"

The words came out of the darkness. He blinked hard. Tired. He was just tired. That was all. He turned to Stephen, there in the gloom. He seemed a thing of shadows. Was he even there? James was tired. But he blinked hard and refocused his vision. "Yeah. How do you feel about Thai food?"

They ran into the restaurant from the rain. It had begun to thunder loudly as they had been walking through the parking lot, and the drops had begun to fall as they'd gotten close, so they'd picked up the pace. Lightning flashed white hot across the sky. The thunder made their chests rumble. It seemed like the end of the world.

"Table for two, please," James told the hostess.

"Right this way," she said, grabbing some menus. She led them to a table, and they settled down soon enough.

And when they were seated, Stephen pointedly said: "What's wrong?"

"Nothing!" James said. He'd been startled. "It's nothing, just..." he rubbed his eyes, "I haven't been getting a lot of sleep, lately."

"I mean, can't blame you, right?" Stephen laughed. "Your wife's out of town. That bed must be pretty lonely right now."

"Right, right," said James, all his nights on the couch hitting him harder than ever.

The waitress brought them some complimentary bowls of soup. Stephen spooned some into his mouth, opening his mouth wide and breathing hard because the soup was hot.

And James felt it all tumble out: "Actually, I'm thinking about selling the company."

"What? Really?" Stephen blinked hard. "Do you really think you're ready for that? That your company is ready for that?"

"I... just..."

"Come on, man."

James stared across the table. Stephen was one of his biggest supporters, despite having been with the company such a short time. He repeatedly talked about the potential he saw in James' company, both publicly and in private. He had worked harder than James had even asked him to, pushing a huge number of new clients and partners James' way since they had met.

"If you sell now," said Stephen, "you'll just be bought out by some big, faceless company that doesn't know how to serve your customers. One that doesn't have your personal touch—and that's one of your most important factors." The waitress came, and Stephen began to order.

Of course, as James looked over the menu, he reflected that Stephen was right. His company did seem to do a number of things frighteningly well. Customer service, in particular, was one of their bright spots. And despite owning the software code at the company's heart, James knew that if he sold, it would be stripped down, and all his accounts and customer relations merged into a faceless conglomerate.

But he felt so tired. So worn down. It was almost like nothing seemed real.

"Are you ready to order?"

He looked up. He seemed to briefly see the waitress as some terrible monster with red eyes and sharp teeth.

But he blinked, and suddenly she was normal again, looking down at him with a somewhat puzzled expression.

Tired.

"I'll... have the Pad Thai," he said, softly.

She took the order down on her notepad, and then was gone.

"You know, you're right," he said when she'd left. "I won't sell. Not yet."

"Atta boy," said Stephen with a smile.

"It was just a thought."

"I mean, you haven't even had the big growth spurt yet, the one we've all modeled out," said Stephen. "Whatever you could get for your company by selling now, it's nothing compared to what you could get for it in a few years' time. And really, what would your wife think?"

Those nights on the couch. Tossing and turning.

"Heh, yeah," said James, putting soup in his mouth to avoid speaking further.

The rain was still coming, just a little. Just sprinkling, just a little.

James sat in his car. His lunch with Stephen had ended an hour ago. His employees had long since returned from their lunch breaks. But he sat there, watching the rain patter against the windshield. Afraid to go in.

It was like his company was in there. Well, of course, it was in there. But it seemed... dangerous. Like a thing that lurked. With eyes that saw. Like the thing that had haunted him those nights on the couch.

He felt a chill down his spine. The thing that he feared. The thing creeping after him. The thing that he'd fought about with his wife over and over. It was his company. This company, which he'd founded with so much passion and determination, had become something terrible.

He looked at the building. It seemed to see him. Eyes gleamed out of windows that lurched to the darkened sky. He felt a terror he'd never known before. He wanted to just start the car and drive away. He almost wanted to run before it was too late. The company—his company—was a monster that was going to eat him and consume him.

It was looking right at him.

He shivered.

Because he knew that even if he drove away, he couldn't escape.

"This isn't why I started a company," he said, slinking low, hoping to avoid the monster's sight. "I thought this would be fun."

And the thunder boomed again.

Author's Afterward

James knows that he can't grow his company on his own, but he doesn't know what help he needs. As a business owner, James believes that he needs to leverage what resources he has available, but he hasn't considered the impact of shoehorning in resources that seem to make sense but become more of a detriment to his business success. Inexperienced himself, James isn't aware of what sort of guidance he needs and is far too busy at work to learn what he doesn't know.

Bringing in family can work, but when it doesn't, the risk and impact are much larger on the business and the relationship. A better solution is to reach out to fractional leadership, where one can get experienced leaders and guidance at a fraction of the cost and commitment.

If James had committed to investing in fractional leadership, he could have had the support he needed to grow, while keeping his sanity.

GEORGE MAYFIELD is the CEO of Frameworks Consortium, a company designed to bring Enterprise to the Entrepreneur.

Find out more at www.frameworksconsortium.com where you can find resources to help your business scale efficiently with a full fractional C-Suite Counsel and Peer Advisory. Don't do business alone!

Frameworks for Business Success

As we close the cover on our thrilling journey through the spine-chilling corridors of business horror with "Scary Stories to Tell in the Boardroom", it's time to take a step towards transforming these tales of terror into narratives of triumph. Conquering your business fears is a formidable feat, but remember, you're not alone in this haunted mansion of entrepreneurship.

To guide you along your path to success, we recommend another groundbreaking resource, "Frameworks for Business Success". This book serves as the silver bullet for your business werewolves, the sunlight for your corporate vampires, and the exorcism for your entrepreneurial demons.

"Frameworks for Business Success" is a compendium of proven strategies and approaches that have helped countless businesses rise from the ashes of their mistakes and missteps. It provides a beacon of light to illuminate the dark corners of running a business, uncovering the hidden traps and showing you the path to safety.

Just as we have journeyed through the business world's haunting tales in "Scary Stories to Tell in the Boardroom", "Frameworks for Business Success" is the next chapter of your adventure. It's your chance to face the horrors, learn from them, and ultimately, shape your own powerful business success story.

So, as we part ways at the end of this chilling expedition, remember: there is no horror that cannot be overcome, no fear that cannot be conquered. Arm yourself with knowledge, gather your courage, and step boldly into the future with "Frameworks for Business Success". Let this be the guiding light that leads you out of the darkness and into the dawn of your business success.

Here's to turning your scary stories into success stories. Until our paths cross again in the pages of "Frameworks for Business Success", let's continue to face our fears and conquer our dreams. Your journey in the thrilling world of business continues!

— George R. Mayfield

Frameworks for Business Success can be found at https://a.co/d/69kCBewor at your local bookshop.

Vetted Service Providers

Now that we have armed you with the knowledge and tools to navigate through the business world's dark corners, it's time to put these learnings into action. And what better way to do so than by joining hands with the very best in the field - the Frameworks Consortium Vetted Service Providers. This chapter serves as your guide to connecting with these esteemed experts, and thereby, creating your own chapter in the annals of business success.

Frameworks Consortium Vetted Service Providers are a select group of industry leaders with a proven track record of helping businesses overcome their fears and pave their path to success. They are the torch bearers who can guide your way through the labyrinth of business challenges. Drawing from their vast well of experience and expertise, they can provide invaluable insights and strategies specific to your unique circumstances.

To inquire about these service providers, simply visit the Frameworks Consortium website. There, you will find out more about our vetted providers along with their areas of expertise. You can also submit a query or request a consultation via our user-friendly interface. Our team is committed to connecting you with the best fit for your business needs and aspirations.

But the journey doesn't stop there. We strongly believe that the best learning comes from experience - not just our own, but also the experiences of others. That's why we are expanding our next volume of "Scary Stories to Tell in the Boardroom" to our growing group of stellar business providers.

If you've navigated through your own business horror story and emerged victorious, or if you're in the process of doing so, we invite you to contribute to our upcoming volume. It's an opportunity to share your unique experiences, insights, and lessons with a community of like-minded professionals. Not only will you be leaving your mark in the business world, but you'll also be playing a crucial role in guiding and inspiring others to conquer their own fears.

So get ready to pen your success story. We are eagerly waiting to hear your tale. Remember, it's not just about overcoming your own business horrors. It's about lighting the way for others to do the same. Let's continue to face our fears, learn from each other, and build a community that thrives on shared success and mutual growth.

Here's to your future chapters in the world of business. Let your journey continue with the Frameworks Consortium and may you turn your business tales of terror into triumphs. And who knows? Your story could be the beacon for many others in the business world, setting the stage for their own success stories.

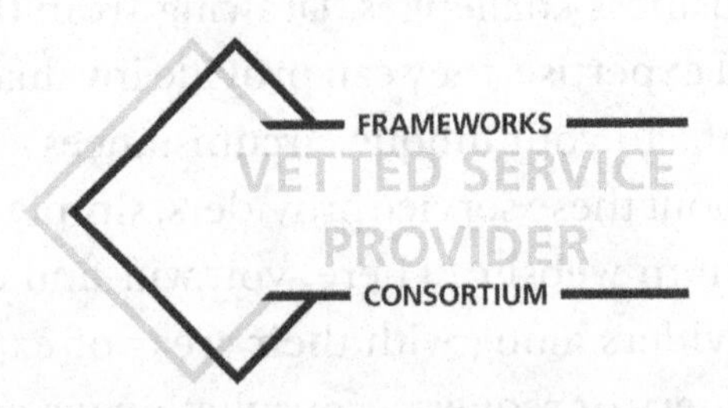

Visit www.frameworksconsortium.com to learn more about our guided strategic growth and Vetted Service Provider programs.

Acknowledgements

I can't publish this book without thanking the authors and artists that came before me and inspired this compilation of twisted business tales. Back when school libraries used punch cards and signatures to check out books, my elementary school library's copy of Scary Stories to Tell in the Dark, by Alvin Schwartz had my name on about 80% of the checkout lines. The artwork by Stephen Gammell haunted my dreams and the stories of ghosts, ghouls, and things that go bump in the night have shaped so much of my life and let my mind feel safe to explore the unexplored.

I'd like to thank Jimbo Mathus, the mad mind behind (and often in front of) the band, Squirrel Nut Zippers. His weird and quirky music inspired me as a teen and does still to this day. It continues to inspire me to look at the world differently.

I owe gratitude to the team of creatives that worked on this project and brought it to life with their imagination and energy. Our collective vision has made all of this possible. Without them this book would never have been completed. From the cover artists, designers, writers- thank you all for sharing in this dream!

So thank you to everyone who has been a part of this journey - from those who've encouraged me to take risks, to those who have laughed with and called out the crazy ideas that never worked. You've all shaped what this book is today and I'm forever grateful.

Thank you for joining us on this wild ride! Let's keep pushing through our fears, keep learning from each other, and keep inspiring one another as we continue on our journeys!

Made in the USA
Monee, IL
16 September 2023